THIS BOOK BELONGS TO:

_____

Getting Back to Me

A Book for Children & Adults on Emotional Regulation.

Written by Joycy Ann Lacombe, LMHC
Thoughtfully Illustrated by Kathleen Motoa

To Isaiah, who doesn't bat an eye to any project or
adventure I share with him, which is evidence
that clearly he believes I can do anything.
I love you dearly!

To my loving parents, sisters, family, village and
trusted crew who provide me the space, the reprieve
and the material to draw from...
My life is so full with you in it.

To Christine, who God placed by my side for a
lifetime to ensure that I pursue my purpose.
This is only a speck on our journey.

To Dianna, my trusted editor and friend who pushes
perfection from every piece of work I produce. I find
rest in surrendering my thoughts and ideas to
your impeccable critique.

And to Kathleen, who inspired me to pursue this
lifelong passion of publishing because she first pursued
her own. Thank you.

I am forever grateful to you all.

When you're feeling nervous, or
scared or sad or blue,
There are lots of helpful things
that you can do...for you.

When I need to relax, I practice breathing from my middle.
My stuffy moving up and down always makes me giggle!

Or I close my eyes and think
of my favorite treat,
imagining the yummy smell as I
breathe in deep.

1, 2, 3, 4....

I hold my breath and count to four,
then slowly breathe it out
once more.

1, 2, 3, 4....

When my thoughts are unkind and
I don't like how they sound,
I use my cool numbers to turn
them around.

I skip and count by 2s, 5s or 10s,
take a deep breath and count
them again.

Or sometimes I count to 10 and
backwards again:

1, 2, 3, 4, 5, 6, 7, 8, 9, 10,
10, 9, 8, 7, 6, 5, 4, 3, 2, 1

This helps slow my thoughts when
they're moving too fast,
and I think better thoughts once
the moment has passed.

When I tap my thumb to my
fingers A, B, C, D...
I feel relaxed and safe inside
my body.

When I can't pay attention, I get moving just for fun.
My brain feels so much better once I've walked or jumped or run!

When I start to feel anxious I tell
myself it won't last.
I think about all the things that
have helped me in the past.

I give myself a great big hug
and let those feelings in,
deep down I know when I choose
love, the anxious thoughts won't
win.

When the thoughts feel so
big and I just want to hide,
I've learned to share my worries
and not keep them all inside.

The thoughts don't feel as
strong when I tell a
parent or a friend,
knowing I'm not alone helps
bring those thoughts to an end.

When confusing thoughts try
to change how I feel,
writing or drawing helps me
know what is real.

My imagination sometimes takes
me on a wild ride,
But *I* get to control how I feel
inside.

I close my eyes and imagine
feeling better tomorrow,
calm and happy and free.

Seeing myself calm in the future
helps me get back to being me!

Joycy Ann Lacombe is a Licensed Mental Health Counselor who specializes in trauma. She is passionate about educating others about the power they have within to challenge their thoughts and create new, healthier ways of thinking, through various evidence-based neurological interventions. Here she combines her passion for writing and teaching, to influence a new wave of emotionally regulated families.

You can find her at IlluminatingHope.org & on Instagram: @Illuminating_Hope

Kathleen Motoa has a BA in Studio Art. She has a love for introducing art to young children and has been teaching art to young minds since 2012. You can follow her incredible ideas on Instagram at @bekindandmakeart. Kathleen has also published several books for young readers, her most recent being, "It's Okay to Have Big Emotions" which can be found on Amazon.

You can find her on Instagram: IG: @kathleenmotoa

Made in the USA
Coppell, TX
28 August 2021